It's Easy To Play The Seventies.

Wise Publications
London/New York/Sydney

Exclusive distributors:
Music Sales Limited
8/9 Frith Street, London W1V 5TZ, England.
Music Sales Pty Limited
120 Rothschild Avenue, Rosebery, NSW 2018, Australia.

This book © Copyright 1990 by
Wise Publications
UK ISBN 0.7119.1327.7
Order No. AM 68354

Art direction by Mike Bell
Cover illustration by Paul Allen
Compiled by Peter Evans
Arranged by Frank Booth

Music Sales' complete catalogue lists thousands of
titles and is free from your local music shop,
or direct from Music Sales Limited.
Please send £1.50 Cheque or Postal Order for postage to
Music Sales Limited, 8/9 Frith Street, London W1V 5TZ.

Printed in the United Kingdom by
Caligraving Limited Thetford Norfolk

Annie's Song

Words & Music by John Denver

At Seventeen

Words & Music by Janis Ian

Moderately

I learned the truth at sev - en - teen ___ that
(A) brown eyed girl in hand - me - downs ___ whose
(To) those of us who know ___ the pain ___ of

love was meant for beau - ty queens ___ and
name I nev - er could ___ pro - nounce, ___ said,
val - en - tines that nev - er came, ___ and

high - school girls ___ with clear - skinned smiles ___ who
"Pi - ty please, ___ the ones ___ who serve, ___ they
those who's names ___ were nev - er called ___ when

mar - ried young and then re - tired. ___
on - ly get what they de - serve." ___
choos - ing sides for bas - ket ball. ___

C

The val - en - tines I nev - er knew, __ the
The rich re - la - tioned home - town queen __ the
It was long a - go and far __ a - way, __ the

Dm   A   Dm   G7

Fri - day night char - ades __ of youth __ were spent on one __ more beau-
mar - ries in to what __ she needs, __ a guar - an - tee __ of com-
world was young - er than __ to - day, __ and dreams were all __ they gave __

C

- ti - ful, __ at sev - en - teen I learned __ the truth. __
- pa - ny __ and ha - ven for the eld - er - ly. __
__ for free __ to ug - ly duck - ling girls __ like me. __

Cmaj9 C Cmaj7   C   Eb

And those of us __ with rav-
Re - mem - ber those __ who win
We all play the game __ and when

Dm7   G7

- aged fac - es, lack - ing in the so - cial gra - ces,
the game __ lose the love they sought __ to gain __ in
__ we dare __ to cheat our - selves at sol - i - taire __ in-

8

Bridge Over Troubled Water

Words & Music by Paul Simon

Like a bridge o-ver troub-led wa-ter, I will lay me

G   C7   F   C dim   C   A7   F   E7

down. Like a bridge o-ver troub-led wa-ter, I will lay me

Am   C7   F   C dim   C   A7   F   G7

tempo rubato

down.   When you're

C   F   C   F

troub-led wa-ter, I will lay me down.   Sail on

C   Am   F   Am E7 Am   F

sil-ver girl,   sail on by.   Your time has come   to shine.

C   F   C   F   Bb F C

11

Bright Eyes

Words & Music by Mike Batt

Oh, is it a dream? There's a

C   Am   D7

no chord

fog a - long the hor - i - zon. A

G   C   G

strange glow in the sky, And

Em   C   G

no - bo - dy seems to know where you go, and what does it

D   D7   G   C

mean? Oh, oh, is it a

B   Gdim   Bm   Am7   D7

dream?_____ Bright___ eyes

G   Bm

burn - ing   like__ fire.____   Bright__

C   D7

eyes   how can you close and   fail.____

Bm   C   Am7

___   How can   the light   that   burned   so   bright - ly

D7   B7   Em   D7   G

sud - den - ly burn so   pale,   Bright__   eyes.____
                                            ritard.

C   Am7   D7   G

Goodbye Yellow Brick Road

Words & Music by Elton John & Bernie Taupin

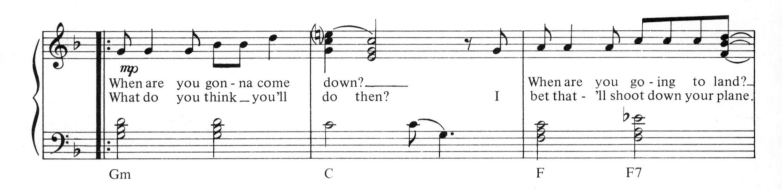

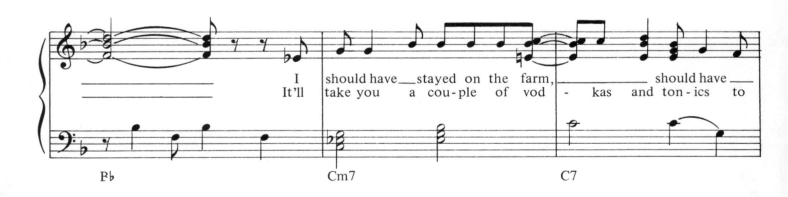

er,_____ I did-n't sign up ___ with you._____ I'm
ment,_____ there's plen-ty like me __ to be found._____

C7   F   B♭   Gm7

not a pre-sent for your friends _ to op - en, this boy's _ too young to be
Mon - grels _____ who ain't got a pen - ny, sing-ing for tit - bits like

E♭   C7   F   C7

sing-ing _____ the blues._____
you ___ on the ground.____   Ah _____

F   D♭   E♭7   A♭

_____   ah _____ So good-bye yel-low brick

D♭   C7   F

road,_____ where the dogs of so - ci - e - ty howl._____ You

A7   B♭   Gm7   F   F7

can't plant me in your pent - house,_____ I'm go-ing back_to my plough.____

D7   Gm   C7   F

Back to the howl-ing old owl ___ in the woods, hunting the horn - y black toad.

Dm   A   Bb   Gm7   Db

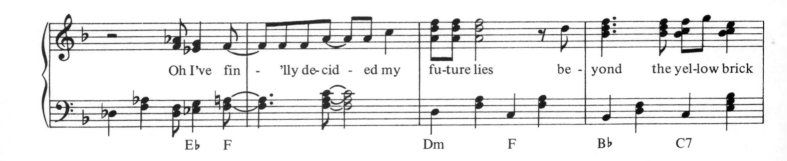

Oh I've fin - 'lly de-cid - ed my fu-ture lies be - yond the yel-low brick

Eb F   Dm   F   Bb   C7

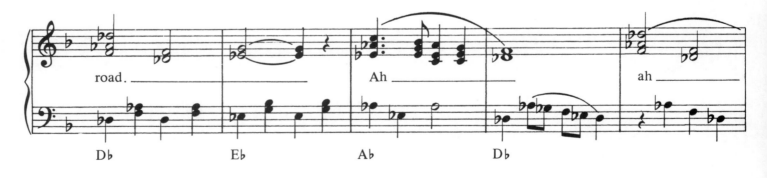

road._____ Ah _____ ah _____

Db   Eb   Ab   Db

Ah _____   Ah.

C7   F   F

Ped.   *

Evergreen

Words by Paul Williams
Music by Barbra Streisand

Moderately, with feeling

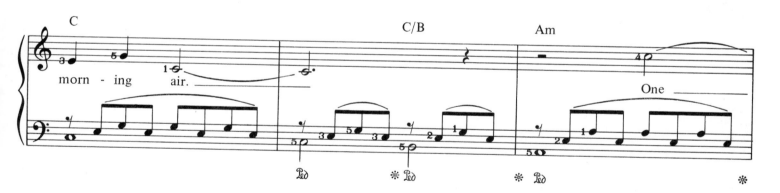

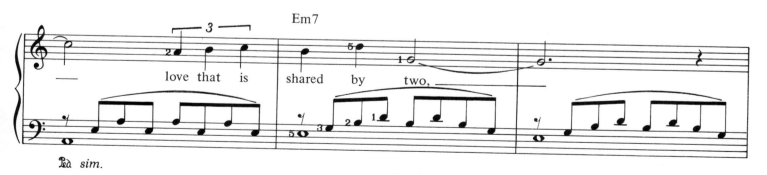

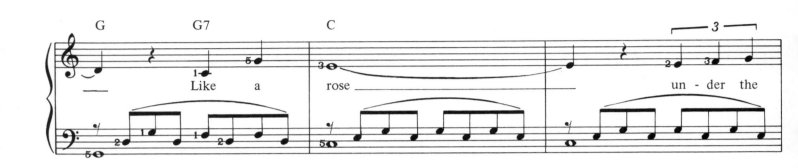

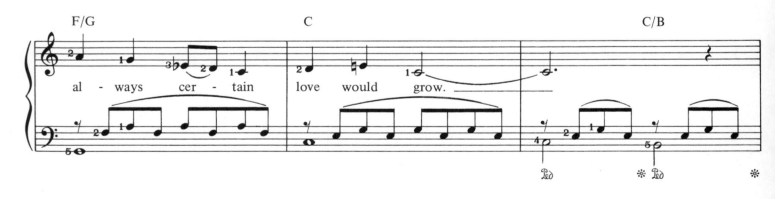

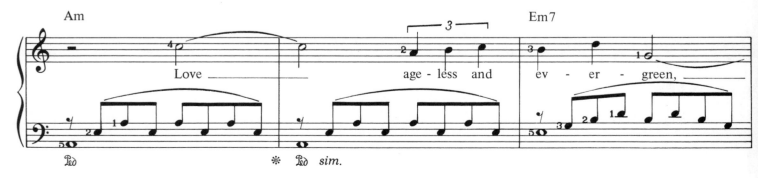

'cause we have the bright - est ... love, ___ two lights that

shine as one, ___ morn - ing,

glo - ry ___ and ___ the ___ mid - night sun. ___

Time, ___ we've learned to sail a - bove; ___

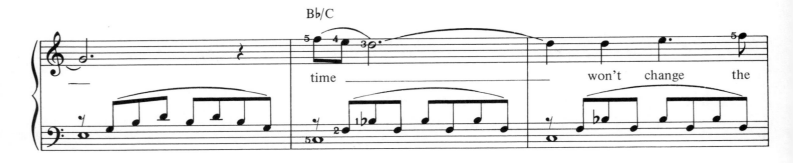

time ___ won't change the

22

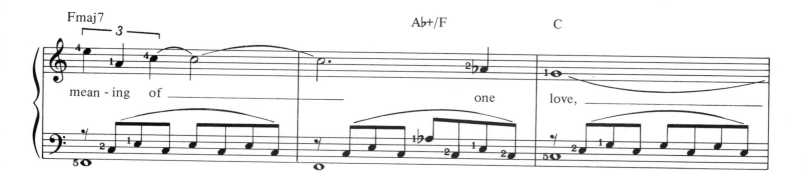

mean - ing   of _____   one   love, _____

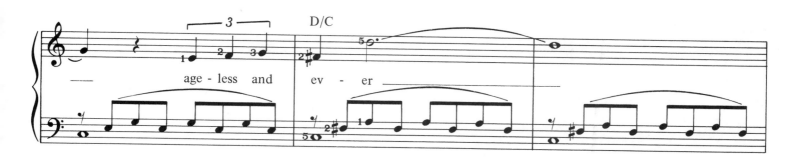

_____   age - less   and   ev - er _____

ev - er _____   green. _____

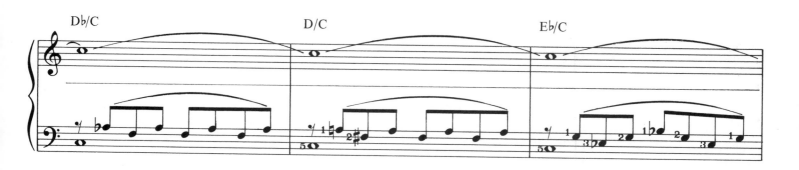

rit. e dim.   *mp*

Miss You Nights

Words & Music by Dave Townsend

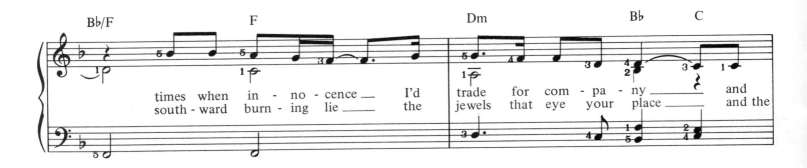

Piano Man

Words & Music by Billy Joel

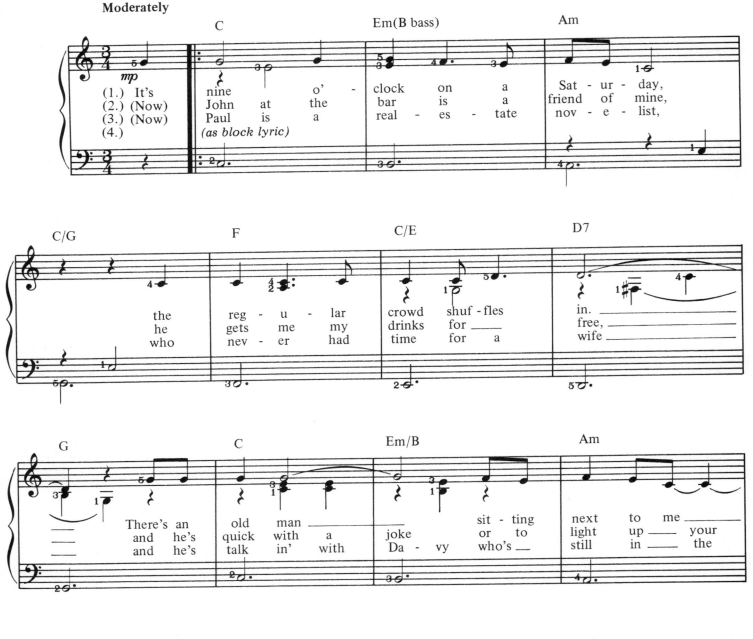

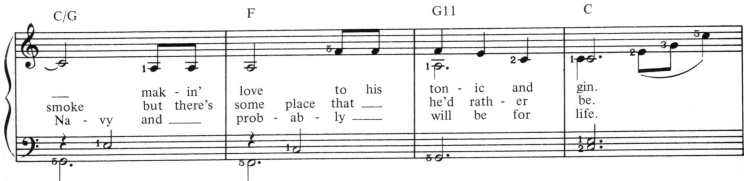

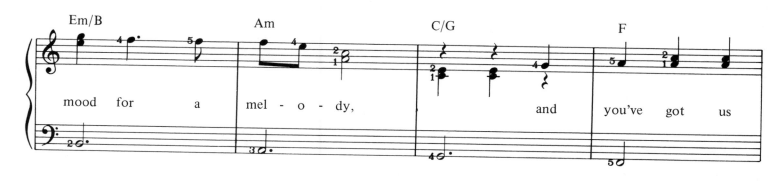

mood for a mel - o - dy, and you've got us

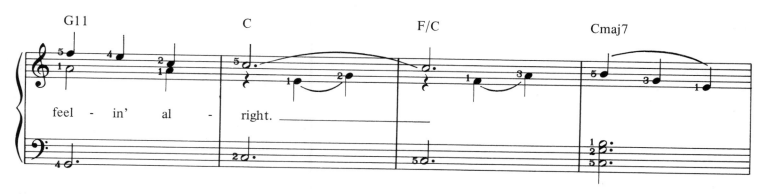

feel - in' al - right. _____

(2.) Now
(3.) Now
(4.) It's a

VERSE 4:
It's a pretty good crowd for a Saturday,
And the manager gives me a smile.
'Cause he knows that it's me they've been coming to see
To forget about life for a while.
And the piano sounds like a carnival
And the microphone smells like a beer,
And they sit at the bar and put bread in my jar
And say "Man what are you doing here?"

Da da da *etc.*

Sailing

Words & Music by Gavin Sutherland

Repeat and fade

The Killing Of Georgie
(Parts I and II)

Words & Music by Rod Stewart

Moderately slow, in 2

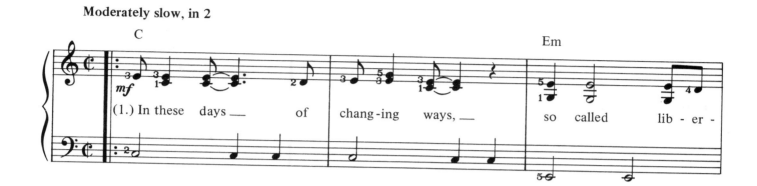

(1.) In these days ___ of chang-ing ways, ___ so called lib-er-

-at-ed days, ___ a sto-ry comes ___ to mind ___ of a friend of mine.

Georg - ie boy ___ was

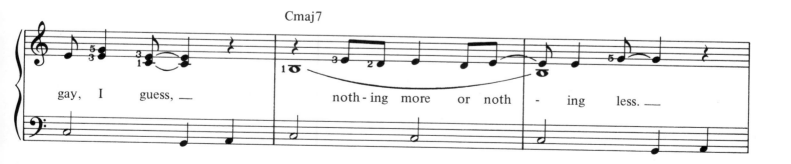

gay, I guess, ___ noth-ing more or noth - ing less. ___

VERSE 2:
His mother's tears fell in vain
The afternoon George tried to explain
That he needed love like all the rest.
Pa said, "There must be a mistake.
How can my son not be straight
After all I've said and done for him?"

VERSE 3:
Leavin' home on a Greyhound bus,
Cast out by the ones he loves,
A victim of these gay days it seems.
Georgie went to New York town
Where he quickly settles down
And soon became the toast of the Great White Way.

VERSE 4:
Accepted by Manhattan's elite
In all the places that were chic,
No party was complete without George.
Along the boulevards he'd cruise
And all the old queens blew a fuse;
Everybody loved Georgie boy.

VERSE 5:
The last time I saw George alive
Was in the summer of '75.
He said he was in love; I said "I'm pleased."
George attended the opening night
Of another Broadway hype,
But split before the final curtain fell.

VERSE 6:
Deciding to take a short cut home,
Arm in arm, they meant no wrong;
A gentle breeze blew down Fifth Avenue.
Out of a darkened side street came
A New Jersey gang with just one aim:
To roll some innocent passerby.

VERSE 7:
There ensued a fearful fight;
Screams rung out in the night.
Georgie's head hit a sidewalk cornerstone.
A leather kid, a switchblade knife,
He did not intend to take his life;
He just pushed his luck a little too far that night.

VERSE 8:
The sight of blood dispersed the gang;
A crowd gathered, the police came,
An ambulance screamed to a halt on Fifty-third and Third.
Georgie's life ended there,
But I ask, who really cares?
George once said to me, and I quote:

VERSE 9:
He said: "Never wait or hesitate.
Get in, kid, before it's too late;
You may never get another chance,
Cause youth's a mask, but it don't last.
Live it long and live it fast."
Georgie was a friend of mine.

To All The Girls I've Loved Before

Words & Music by Hal David & Albert Hammond

2.

G

The wind of change are al-ways
cresc.

C/G   G

blow - ing ____

and ev-'ry time I tried to

Am7

stay.

Am7/D

The winds of change con - tin - ued

D7   Am7/D   D7   G   C/G

blow - ing, ____

and they just car-ried me a - way.
dim.

D.%. al Coda

G

(3.) To all the girls who

⊕ CODA

Eb

loved

F

be - fore.

G

Year Of The Cat

Words & Music by Al Stewart & Peter Wood

in - cense and patch - ou - li. So you take her _____ to

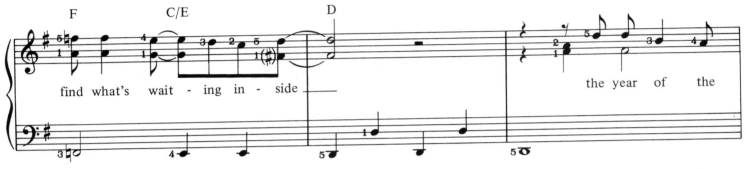

find what's wait - ing in - side _____ the year of the

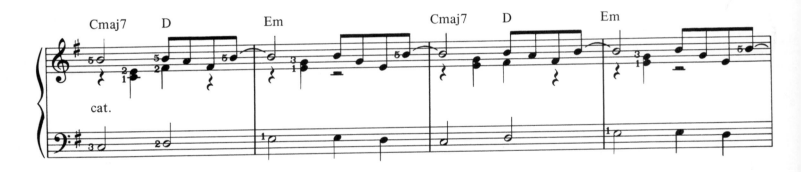

cat.

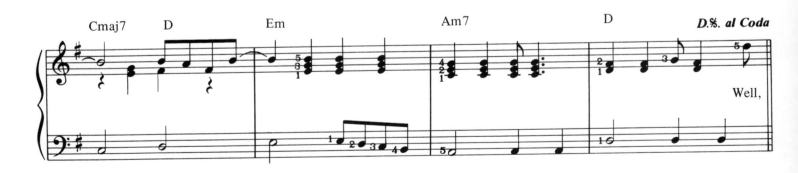

Well,

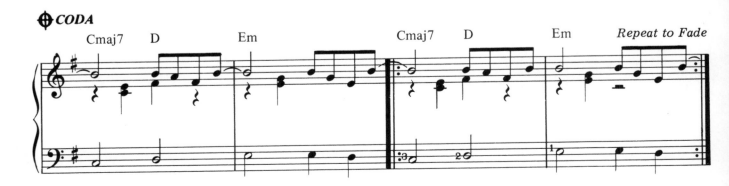

42

Thank You For The Music

Words & Music by Benny Andersson & Bjorn Ulvaeus

We Don't Talk Anymore

Words & Music by Alan Tarney

Moderately

(1.) Used to think that life was sweet ___
(2.) (used) to feel we had it made ___
(3.) real - ly does - n't matter to me ___

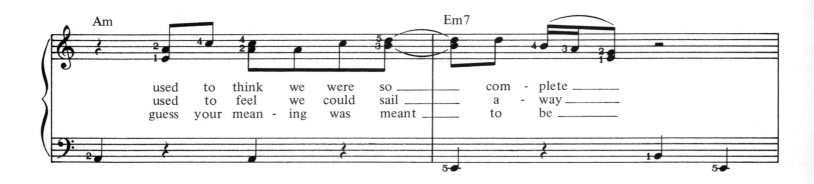

used to think we were so ___ com - plete ___
used to feel we could sail ___ a - way ___
guess your mean - ing was meant ___ to be ___

I can't be - lieve ___ you'd throw it a - way.
can you im - ag - ine how I feel to - day.
it's down to you now you want to be free.

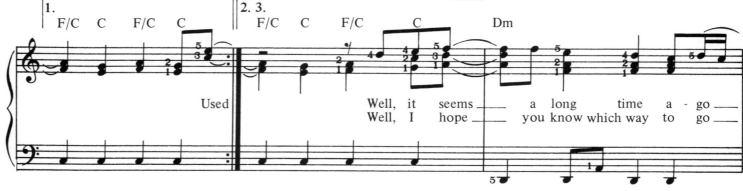

1. F/C C F/C C

Used

2. 3. F/C C F/C C Dm

Well, it seems ___ a long time a - go ___
Well, I hope ___ you know which way to go ___

an - y -more

but I ain't los - ing sleep

And I ain't count-ing sheep.

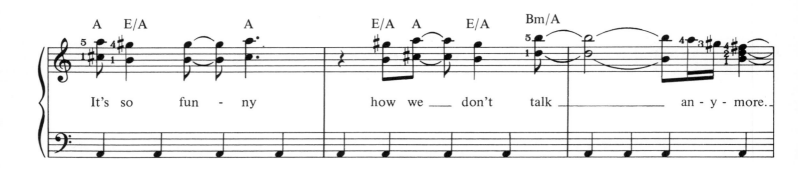

It's so   fun – ny

how we ___ don't   talk _____ an - y - more.

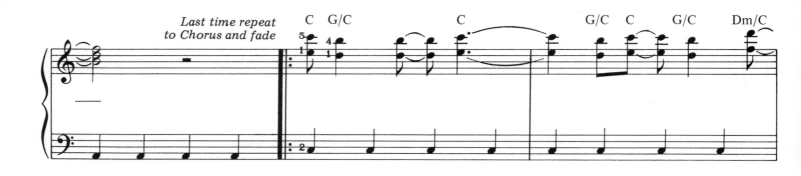

*Last time repeat
to Chorus and fade*

Well it

9/93 (16127)